WEST HAM UNITED LONDON

THE OFFICIAL 2019/20
HAMMERS
YEARBOOK

Contributors:
Peter Rogers & Rob Mason

A TWOCAN PUBLICATION

©2019. Published by twocan
under licence from West Ham United FC.

ISBN: 978-1-912692-54-5

PICTURE CREDITS: Action Images, Getty Images, Griffiths Photographers, Press Association.

3

WEST HAM UNITED LONDON

2019

AUGUST 2019

Saturday	10	Manchester City	H
Saturday	17	Brighton and Hove Albion	A
Saturday	24	Watford	A
Tuesday	27	Newport County	A	EFL Cup 2
Saturday	31	Norwich City	H

SEPTEMBER 2019

Monday	16	Aston Villa	A
Sunday	22	Manchester United	H
Wednesday	25	Oxford United	A	EFL Cup 3
Saturday	28	Bournemouth	A

OCTOBER 2019

Saturday	05	Crystal Palace	H
Saturday	19	Everton	A
Saturday	26	Sheffield United	H
W/C	28			EFL Cup 4

NOVEMBER 2019

Saturday	02	Newcastle United	H
Saturday	09	Burnley	A
Saturday	23	Tottenham Hotspur	H
Saturday	30	Chelsea	A

DECEMBER 2019

Tuesday	03	Wolverhampton Wanderers	A
Saturday	07	Arsenal	H
Saturday	14	Southampton	A
W/C	16			EFL Cup 5
Saturday	21	Liverpool*	H	Postponed*
Thursday	26	Crystal Palace	A
Saturday	28	Leicester City	H

*Match to be rescheduled due to Liverpool's participation in the FIFA Club World Cup.

6

PREMIER LEAGUE FIXTURES

2020

WEST HAM UNITED · LONDON

JANUARY 2020

Wednesday	01	Bournemouth	H	
Saturday	04			FA Cup 3
W/C	06			EFL Cup SF1
Saturday	11	Sheffield United	A	
Saturday	18	Everton	H	
Tuesday	21	Leicester City	A	
Saturday	25			FA Cup 4
W/C	27			EFL Cup SF2

FEBRUARY 2020

Saturday	01	Brighton and Hove Albion	H
Saturday	08	Manchester City	A
Saturday	22	Liverpool	A
Saturday	29	Southampton	H

MARCH 2020

Sunday	01			EFL Cup F
Wednesday	04			FA Cup 5
Saturday	07	Arsenal	A	
Saturday	14	Wolverhampton Wanderers	H	
Saturday	21	Tottenham Hotspur	A	FAC6

APRIL 2020

Saturday	04	Chelsea	H	
Saturday	11	Newcastle United	A	
Saturday	18	Burnley	H	FAC SF
Saturday	25	Norwich City	A	

MAY 2020

Saturday	02	Watford	H	
Saturday	09	Manchester United	A	
Sunday	17	Aston Villa	H	
Saturday	23			FA Cup Final

8

BACK (L TO R): James Saban (Kit Manager), Xavi Valero (GK Coach), Ben Johnson, Winston Reid, Andriy Yarmolenko, Sebastien Haller, Issa Diop, Declan Rice, Angelo Ogbonna, Fabián Balbuena, Michail Antonio, Gonçalo Cardoso, Nathan Holland, Hugo Scheckter (Head of Player Care), Jamie Osman (Head of Performance Analysis).

MIDDLE (L TO R): Richard Collinge (Head of Medical Services), Mario Husillos (Director of Football), Carlos Sánchez, Robert Snodgrass, Ryan Fredericks, Joseph Anang, Lukasz Fabianski, Roberto, David Martin, Chicharito (Transferred), Xande Silva, Albian Ajeti, Felix Cao (Assistant Fitness Coach), Jose Cabello (Fitness Coach).

FRONT (L TO R): Conor Coventry, Arthur Masuaku, Aaron Cresswell, Felipe Anderson, Mark Noble (Captain), Ruben Cousillas (Assistant Coach), Manuel Pellegrini (First Team Manager), Enzo Maresca (Second Assistant Coach), Pablo Zabaleta, Manuel Lanzini, Jack Wilshere, Pablo Fornals.

HAMMER OF THE YEAR

Lukasz FABIANSKI

Lukasz Fabianski did not just walk away from the West Ham United Awards evening at the InterContinental London - the 02 - with the Betway Hammer of the Year award, the Poland international also collected the awards as Signing of the Season and Save of the Season.

"I'm very happy obviously, and very grateful for all the fans who voted for me" said the stopper who delightedly added, "It's something special, especially in my first season here, so I really appreciate all the support. I'm just happy that I've been able to perform in the way that they can see me as a good goalkeeper."

Fabianski became the first goalkeeper since Rob Green in 2008 to be named Hammer of the Year. He joined a select group of goalies to receive the accolade: Shaka Hislop, Ludek Miklosko, Phil Parkes and Lawrie Leslie being the others.

Quick off his line, good on one-on-ones and excellent in terms of his anticipation and reading of the game, Lukasz made a number of outstanding saves. One handed stops low to his right from Callum Wilson of Bournemouth and Manchester United's Marouane Fellaini stood out, the latter taking the accolade of Save of the Season.

Ever-present in the Premier League, Lukasz kept his first clean sheet in a goalless draw with Chelsea adding his first on the road in a handsome 3-0 win at Newcastle. The 'keeper kept seven shut-outs in total including key clean sheets in single-goal victories over both Spurs and Arsenal. No doubt buoyed by being named Betway Hammer of the Year, Fabianski was also unbeaten in two summer internationals for Poland.

Thankfully, Fabianski was not the only man in fine form throughout 2018/19, Declan Rice being runner-up as Hammer of the Year for the second successive season and also picking up the Young Hammer of the Year for a third season in a row as well as collecting the Players' Player of the Year award. Rice even emulated Fabianski in picking up a third award as the midfielder collected the Best Individual Performance accolade for his display at home to Arsenal.

Fabianski's fabulous save from Fellaini was part of the 'Best Team Performance' of the season against Manchester United while Anderson's brilliant goal against Crystal Palace won him the Goal of the Season title.

Proving, once an Irons legend, always an Irons legend, Ronnie Boyce was the recipient of the Lifetime Achievement Award.

Lukasz's lifetime in football may have seemed to be largely over, when he arrived at London Stadium in the summer of 2018 having just passed his 34th birthday, but as a goalkeeper, he is just reaching his peak and hopefully will go on to enjoy several more seasons as the Hammers' number one.

2019/20

PRE-SEASON PREPARATIONS

Ahead of a challenging opening-day fixture with treble-winning Manchester City, Manuel Pellegrini's Hammers played half-a-dozen pre-season warm-up matches including a dress rehearsal meeting with City in the Premier League Asia Trophy.

West Ham United kicked-off their 2019/20 pre-season schedule with an entertaining 3-2 win over SCR Altach in Austria on 11 July 2019. The Hammers travelled over the border from their Swiss training camp in Bad Ragaz to take on the team which finished eighth in the Austrian Bundesliga last season.

Pellegrini handed a debut to goalkeeper Roberto, but it was one of his first signings, Carlos Sánchez, who headed the Londoners in front from Robert Snodgrass' left-wing corner inside six minutes. After some patient passing in their own half, Mark Noble launched the Hammers forward with a long, straight ball over the Altach defence. Michail Antonio broke the offside trap, rounded goalkeeper Martin Kobras and slotted in his side's second of the game.

Ben Johnson then clipped the crossbar with a curler, but Altach kept at it, to their credit, and halved the arrears moments later when Emir Karic's low cross was swept home by the lively Manfred Fischer. Three minutes after the break, Altach levelled the game when Christian Gebauer confidently converted after good work down the right flank from Brazilian full-back Anderson.

The game continued to ebb and flow until the fifth and final goal of the game arrived on 58 minutes. The returning Andriy Yarmolenko, who was one of eight substitutes introduced at half-time, won a corner on the right. The set-piece was taken short and another substitute, Jack Wilshere, delivered a left-footed cross for Issa Diop to stoop and head past Kobras from twelve yards.

All in all, it was a decent workout for Pellegrini's men in front of an enthusiastic crowd of 2,981, including a good number of loyal and vociferous Hammers supporters.

Following their victory over Altach, the Irons switched their attentions to the Premier League Asia Trophy in China, but West Ham's hopes of winning a first Premier League Asia Trophy were ended by treble-winners Manchester City in the Olympic Sports Centre on 17 July.

Wearing their smart navy third kit and with a special 'Hammers' message displayed on their shirts in Mandarin, the Londoners made a fine start and led through Noble's first-half penalty, only for two goals in the space of three minutes, from David Silva and a Lukas Nmecha penalty, to give Pep Guardiola's side the lead by the interval.

And, following the introduction of a succession of City's top international players in place of the youngsters who kicked-off the game, the Premier League champions added two further Raheem Sterling goals and ran out comfortable 4-1 winners.

Despite the scoreline and muggy conditions, West Ham kept going and were nearly rewarded late in the game when Chicharito's free-kick was kept out by Claudio Bravo and Yarmolenko put the follow-up against the outside of the post from a tight angle.

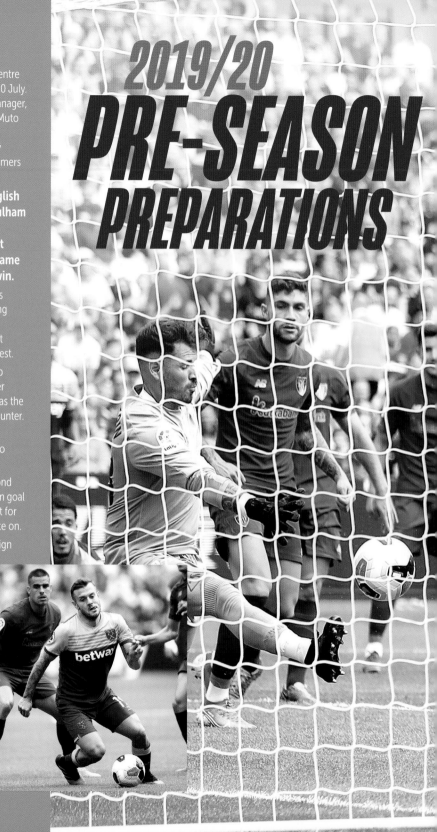

2019/20 PRE-SEASON PREPARATIONS

Defeat resulted in West Ham taking on Newcastle United - beaten 4-0 by Wolverhampton Wanderers in the first semi-final at the Olympic Sports Centre Stadium - in the third-place play-off at Shanghai's Hongkou Stadium on 20 July. The match against Newcastle saw the opposition's recently appointed manager, Steve Bruce, watch on from the stands as a first-half goal from Yoshinori Muto proved enough to condemn the Hammers to their second defeat of the tournament. The 2019 Premier League Asia Trophy was eventually won by Wolves who beat Manchester City on penalties in the final, while the Hammers ended the tournament in fourth place.

West Ham played their first game of the 2019/20 season on English soil when they made the short trip to Craven Cottage to face Fulham on Saturday, 27 July. The hard work on the training fields in Switzerland, China and at Rush Green was evident from the first whistle, and Lanzini's stunning finish was enough to see off a game Fulham side and claim a second pre-season victory with a 1-0 win.

In a match where Sebastien Haller and Pablo Fornals made their Hammers debuts, it was West Ham's resident jewel that proved the difference, curling home a spectacular strike from the edge of the box on 18 minutes. Haller himself went close to doubling the lead in the second half, seeing his shot somehow kept out, while Antonio also went close in an entertaining contest.

Pellegrini's men were on their travels again, ending July with a second trip to Austria. This time to face German side Hertha Berlin on July 31. Summer singings Fornals and Haller each netted their first West Ham United goals as the Irons came from behind to win 5-3 in what was a thrilling pre-season encounter.

The Hammers had to twice equalise in the first half, the first coming from Fornals' left-footed finish, before Lanzini powered home his second in two games just prior to the half-hour mark.

Hertha Berlin took the lead for the third time, seven minutes into the second period, only for Haller to level once again, heading home his first West Ham goal after Snodgrass' brilliant free-kick. On 78 minutes, West Ham went in front for the first time through Grady Diangana, before Antonio secured the win late on.

West Ham's final encounter ahead of the 2019/20 Premier League campaign saw Athletic Bilbao claim the Betway Cup on penalties after an thoroughly entertaining 2-2 draw at London Stadium on Saturday 3 August.

All the goals came within the opening 23 thrilling minutes, as Bilbao moved into a two-goal lead through Haller's own-goal and Inaki Williams' close range finish. West Ham came roaring back with two goals of their own inside 85 remarkable seconds. Lanzini notched his third pre-season goal before Wilshere levelled the match.

Somewhat surprisingly, that marked the end of the goalscoring and after Chicharito and Diangana missed from the spot, Yuri Berchiche's successful penalty sealed a 4-2 shootout success for the visitors.

WEST HAM UNITED
LONDON

15

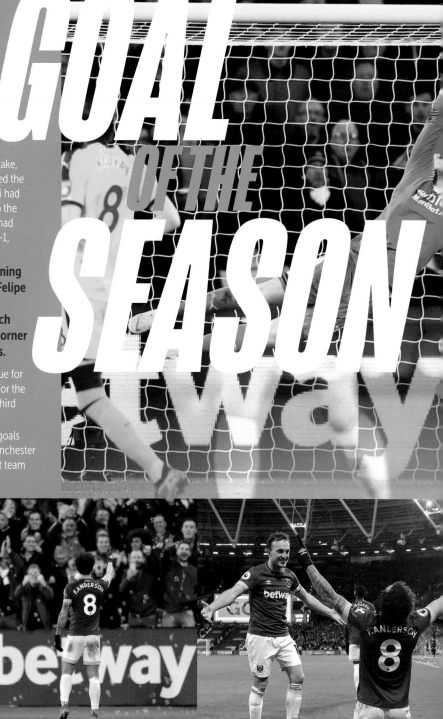

Perhaps Felipe Anderson did not realise the Goal of the Season award was for the whole team to compete for? The braziliant Brazilian scored three of the eight goals nominated for the award, and any one of his top trio would have been a worthy winner.

Felipe's fabulous curled shot against Crystal Palace was the icing on a cake, completing a second-half turnaround against the Eagles who had started the second period at London Stadium a goal to the good. Manuel Pellegrini had evidently had some words of wisdom at half-time and Irons returned to the arena with much more intent. Within three minutes, Robert Snodgrass had levelled the scores and just passed the hour mark, Chicharito made it 2-1, pouncing onto a rebound when Anderson's shot was too hot to hold.

Within three minutes came Felipe's Goal of the Season. Returning the favour, Chicharito displayed great vision to see and find Felipe free on the left of the box. Receiving the Mexican's pass, the Brazilian took a touch to set the ball and with his second touch produced a precise shot that deliciously curled into the top corner of the goal, leaving Palace 'keeper Wayne Hennessey helpless.

Three-one up within 20 minutes of the re-start, West Ham were full value for the three points regardless of Jeffrey Schlupp later pulling a goal back for the visitors. A fine performance lifted the team to tenth in the table after a third successive victory.

Felipe's crystal clear quality was further in evidence with his other two goals short-listed for the Goal of the Season gong. His clever flick against Manchester United was a goal of beauty, while his forceful finish that capped a swift team break away to Southampton was another exceptional strike.

No-one else managed more than one nomination, but there were five other great goals shortlisted. These were Marko Arnautovic's shot at Arsenal, Andriy Yarmolenko's quality strike that beat England 'keeper Jordan Pickford at Everton and Ryan Fredericks' power-drive in the 8-0 thrashing of Macclesfield. Also nominated were Robert Snodgrass' goal at Fulham and Declan Rice's first goal for the club against Arsenal at home, an intuitive shot that found the top corner.

All eight were beautiful to watch, but for Felipe to have three short-listed strikes, shows that not only is the former Lazio and Santos player a terrific team-player, but he possesses the sort of star quality you hope to acquire when you invest a club record fee to bring a Brazil international playmaker to East London. A gold medallist with Brazil at the 2016 Olympics, Felipe's form for West Ham has been rewarded with selection for his first full cap since 2015.

FELIPE ANDERSON

WEST HAM UNITED 3
CRYSTAL PALACE 2

8 December 2018 · London Stadium

THE LEGEND

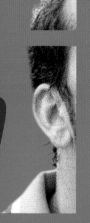

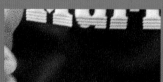

PAOLO DI CANIO

Italian maverick Paulo Di Canio soon won the hearts and minds of the Hammers' fans, and scored his first goal for the club in just his fourth outing during a 2-0 victory over Blackburn Rovers. In total, Di Canio made 13 Premier League appearances following his arrival from Sheffield Wednesday in the middle of the 1998/99 season and his five goals and countless assists helped the Hammers to a fifth-place Premier League finish, that in-turn saw the club qualify for the UEFA Cup through a successful Intertoto Cup campaign.

Di Canio certainly provided the West Ham faithful with many memorable moments during his time in claret and blue. Boss Harry Redknapp once said of his Italian superstar; "He can do things with the ball that other people can only dream of." One of those special moments came in March 2000 when he netted an outstanding flying volley against Wimbledon at the Boleyn Ground. The goal won the BBC Goal of the Season award and is widely regarded as one of the most spectacular goals ever scored in Premier League history.

With 18 goals in his first full season at the Boleyn Ground, including the aforementioned Goal of the Season strike against the Dons, Di Canio was the club's top scorer and played a massive role in the Hammers' ninth-place finish in the Premier League. Of his 18 goals, 16 came in the Premier League and remain a record haul for any West Ham player in the Premier League. Di Canio was subsequently rewarded with the Hammer of the Year award at the end of an outstanding 1999/2000 campaign.

Never far from the headlines throughout his career, Di Canio was involved in a remarkable incident in December 2000 during the Hammers' Premier League match with Everton at Goodison Park. With the match all-square and both sides vying for a winning goal, Di Canio shunned a goalscoring opportunity and stopped play by grabbing the ball following a cross, once he had noticed that Toffee's 'keeper Paul Gerrard was injured after twisting his knee following a clearance. A tremendous demonstration of sportsmanship which was rewarded with a FIFA Fair Play Award.

Since leaving West Ham in 2003, Paulo Di Canio has been a popular attraction whenever he has returned to the club. He played in Tony Carr's testimonial match in 2010, and also received a massive reception from a full house at the Boleyn Ground when he took to the pitch during Mark Noble's testimonial match in 2016 during the final season at famous old ground. Di Canio remains one of the most popular players to represent the club in the modern era and his performances certainly left a mark on those fortunate enough to have witnessed him in action for the Hammers.

WEST HAM UNITED
LONDON

BURNLEY
TURF MOOR
CAPACITY: 22,546

MANCHESTER CITY
ETIHAD STADIUM
CAPACITY: 55,097

MANCHESTER UTD
OLD TRAFFORD
CAPACITY: 76,000

EVERTON
GOODISON PARK
CAPACITY: 39,572

LIVERPOOL
ANFIELD
CAPACITY: 54,074

LEICESTER CITY
KING POWER STADIUM
CAPACITY: 32,312

WOLVES
MOLINEUX STADIUM
CAPACITY: 31,700

ASTON VILLA
VILLA PARK
CAPACITY: 42,785

WATFORD
VICARAGE ROAD
CAPACITY: 21,577

SOUTHAMPTON
ST MARY'S STADIUM
CAPACITY: 32,384

BOURNEMOUTH
VITALITY STADIUM
CAPACITY: 11,329

NEWCASTLE UTD
ST JAMES' PARK
CAPACITY: 52,405

Tick off all 20 Premier League Football Grounds as you follow the Hammers through the 2019/20 campaign.

WEST HAM UNITED LONDON

PREMIER LEAGUE GROUNDS
2019/20

SHEFFIELD UTD
BRAMALL LANE
CAPACITY: 32,702

NORWICH CITY
CARROW ROAD
CAPACITY: 27,244

ARSENAL
EMIRATES STADIUM
CAPACITY: 60,260

TOTTENHAM HOTSPUR
TOTTENHAM HOTSPUR STADIUM
CAPACITY: 62,062

WEST HAM UTD
LONDON STADIUM
CAPACITY: 62,000

CRYSTAL PALACE
SELHURST PARK
CAPACITY: 25,456

CHELSEA
STAMFORD BRIDGE
CAPACITY: 41,631

BRIGHTON & HA
AMERICAN EXPRESS COMMUNITY STADIUM
CAPACITY: 30,666

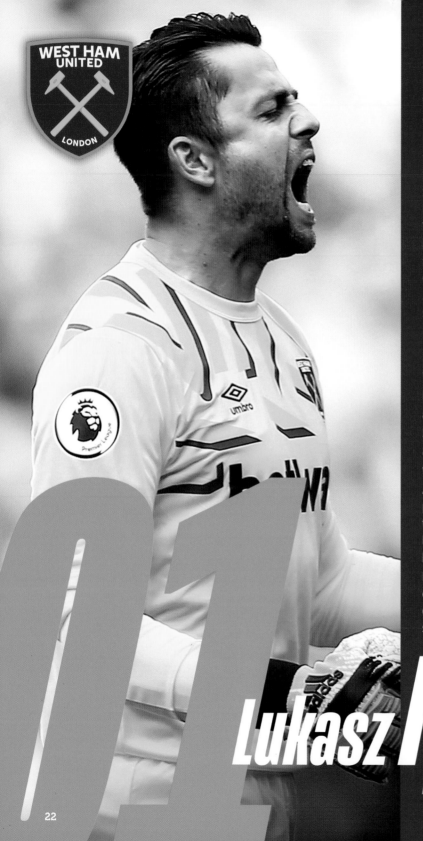

Hammer of the Year for 2018/19, Lukasz Fabianski made more saves than any other Premier League goalkeeper in what was his first season with the Irons. In an ever-present campaign, he was also voted 'Signing of the Season'.

Fabianski was also ever-present as Legia Warsaw took the Polish league title, the Ekstraklasa, in 2005/06. He was beaten just 17 times in the 30 fixtures when he was voted the best keeper in the Ekstraklasa, an award which he retained the following year. Before joining Legia, Fabianski had been with six other Polish outfits as a young player.

The first of what has become over 50 international appearances came in 2006, preceding a place in that year's World Cup finals squad. The following year, Lukasz moved to Arsenal where he enjoyed some fine Champions League performances and an FA Cup winners medal in 2014. Shortly after the Wembley final he joined Swansea, spending four seasons at the Liberty Stadium and being voted their Player of the Year in his final campaign.

New Zealand-born and a full international with the Maoris, Winston also represented Denmark at U19, U20 and U21 level having moved their as a ten-year old with his mother and Danish step-father. He started playing for SUB Sonderborg before joining Midtjylland, making his debut as a 17-year-old.

With the quality to attract interest, Reid joined West Ham United in August 2010, debuting that month against Aston Villa. Initially a fringe player with a dozen appearances in his first campaign as he acclimatised to English football, the following year he played four times as many league games as the Irons bounced back into the Premier League having gone down in Winston's first term.

Reid earned the Hammer of the Year accolade in 2012/13 and continued to play a key role in the squad, later scoring the farewell goal at the Boleyn Ground in May 2016. As of October 2019 Reid was still recuperating from a serious knee injury suffered 18 months earlier.

Lukasz FABIANSKI

POSITION: *Goalkeeper*   DoB: *18 April 1985*   BIRTHPLACE: *Kostrzyn nad Odr, Poland*

02

Winston **REID**

POSITION: *Defender*   DoB: *3 July 1988*   BIRTHPLACE: *North Shore, Auckland, New Zealand*

PREMIER LEAGUE

SQUAD

19/20

23

WEST HAM UNITED
LONDON

03

Aaron CRESSWELL

POSITION: *Defender* DoB: *15 December 1989* BIRTHPLACE: *Liverpool*

PREMIER LEAGUE
SQUAD
19/20

24

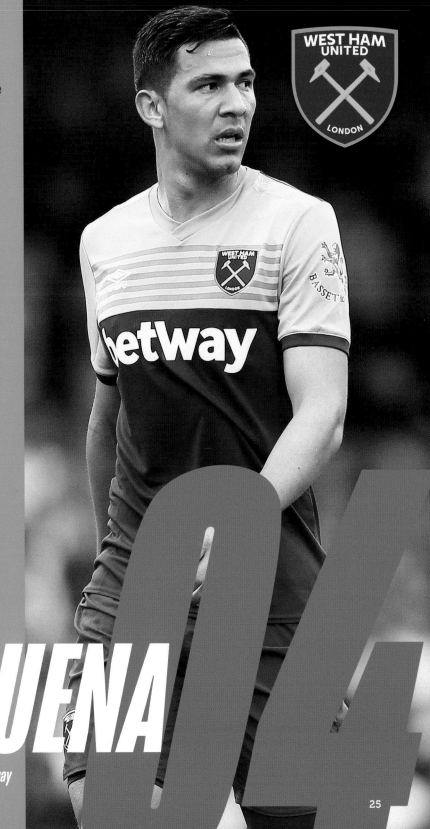

An outstanding piece of transfer business, since arriving from Ipswich Town in July 2014, Cresswell has gone on to become a full England international as well as collecting the 2014/15 Hammer of the Year and Players' Player of the Year awards in his first season.

Cresswell's consistent quality saw him miss only one Premier League game during his first two seasons at the club and just two in his fourth campaign, after a season where he was restricted to 26 league outings due to a knee-ligament injury.

The Merseysider began his career with Tranmere Rovers, breaking into their side in November 2008 before moving on to Ipswich Town in the summer of 2011 where he also became the club's Player of the Year in his first season with the Tractor Boys.

The Paraguay international centre-back is now in the second year of a three-year contract at London Stadium. He debuted on the opening day of the 2018/19 campaign at Anfield and remained a regular member of the side until Christmas when a knee injury kept him out of the action until March.

Returning to the Irons line-up at Chelsea, shortly after proving his fitness with Paraguay in Peru, Balbuena remained an integral part of the defence until the end of the season. His first campaign was extended until the end of June due to his involvement in the Copa America, Paraguay bowing out at the quarter-final stage, losing 4-3 on penalties to eventual champions Brazil.

It was in 2010 that Fabián began his career with Cerro Porteno PF, captaining the team to promotion in his second season. A brief move to Rubio Nu followed, before he was snapped up by reigning champions Club Nacional where he reached the Copa Libertadores finals in 2014.

Two years later, he left Paraguay to play in Brazil with Corinthians winning a trio of trophies before moving to West Ham United.

Fabián BALBUENA 04

POSITION: *Defender* DoB: *23 August 1991* BIRTHPLACE: *Ciudad del Este, Paraguay*

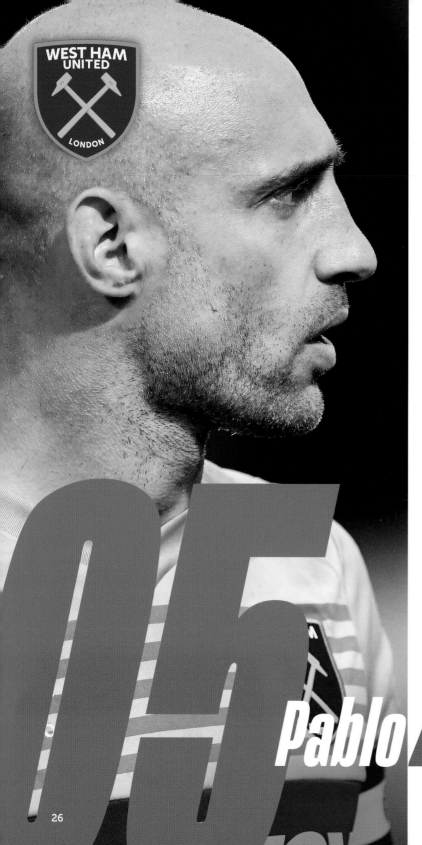

Brilliant at getting forward, Pablo is a vastly-experienced player who has appeared 58 times for his country. He captained Argentina to success at the FIFA U20 World Cup in the Netherlands, won a gold medal at the 2008 Olympics and played in the senior 2014 World Cup in South Africa.

Now in his third season with the Hammers, the 2019/20 campaign is Zabaleta's 12th successive season in the Premier League. His previous campaigns were with Manchester City where for a while he worked with Manuel Pellegrini. A member of the 2012/13 PFA Premier League Team of the Year, he won two Premier League titles during his time with City as well as the FA Cup and two League Cup winner's medals.

After starting his career in his home country with San Lorenzo and prior to coming to England, Pablo enjoyed three seasons in Spain with Espanyol winning the Copa del Rey and playing in the 2007 UEFA Cup final.

Bought from Borussia Dortmund in July 2018, Yarmolenko quickly illustrated his undoubted talent with two goals in the 3-1 at Everton, before tearing his achilles in October and prematurely curtailing his Hammers career.

Returning at the start of the this season, Yarmolenko was quickly back on the goals trail against Norwich and hopefully will go on to enjoy an injury-free season enabling him to rediscover his best form.

The Ukraine international spent a single season in Germany with Borussia Dortmund, during which he scored against Tottenham Hotspur in the Champions League and at Bayern Munich in the Bundesliga. Previously he had hit 99 goals in 228 league appearances for Dynamo Kiev, plus a further 15 goals in 62 games in European competition.

A three-time Ukrainian Premier League winner, Yarmolenko also won three cup competitions in the Ukraine, and was Footballer of the Year four years out of five between 2013 and 2017.

Pablo ZABALETA

POSITION: *Defender* **DoB:** *16 January 1985* **BIRTHPLACE:** *Buenos Aires*

07

WEST HAM
UNITED
LONDON

betway

PREMIER LEAGUE

SQUAD

19/20

Andriy **YARMOLENKO**

POSITION: *Forward* DoB: *23 October 1989* BIRTHPLACE: *Leningrad, (Now St. Petersburg)*

WEST HAM UNITED
LONDON

Felipe ANDERSON

08

POSITION: *Forward* DoB: *15 April 1993* BIRTHPLACE: *Santa Maria DF, Brazil*

PREMIER LEAGUE SQUAD 19/20

The Irons blasted their transfer record to buy Brazil international Felipe in July 2018, for a reported fee of £36m. By the end of his first season, the former Santos and Lazio player had shown he was well worth the investment.

There had been glimpses of Felipe's flair before he scored his first goal, a cute back-heel, in a terrific home win over Manchester United. When he scored in the return fixture in April, it took him into double figures, but Anderson's ability cannot be measured in statistics alone. Very easy on the eye, Felipe is technically excellent and can still apply exquisite touches when running at speed. With the freedom to drift wide or cut inside, he is difficult to pick up and therefore a major asset in the Irons armoury.

A winner of the Copa Libertadores and Recopa Sudamericana with Santos, he picked up more silverware with Lazio, winning the Italian Super Cup in 2017, after winning gold at the 2016 Olympics in his home country.

With his superb close control and willingness to take people on, Lanzini has the ability to excite and get people off their seats. He initially joined West Ham in 2015 on loan from Al-Jazira Club after spending a season in the UAE.

Scoring on his debut in the Europa League and in his second game in the Premier League made him an instant hero, not least as the Premier strike came in a 3-0 victory at Liverpool. A winner against Tottenham Hotspur was a highlight of his second year with the Hammers when he was voted the Players' Player of the Year and runner-up as Hammer of the Year. His continued progress in 2019 was rewarded with a new contract keeping him at London Stadium until 2023.

The Argentina international comes from a footballing family, both his father and brother played professionally, while he won honours in his home country and Brazil during his early years with River Plate and Fluminense.

Manuel LANZINI
10

POSITION: *Midfielder* **DoB:** *15 February 1993* **BIRTHPLACE:** *Buenos Aires*

Robert
SNODGRASS

POSITION: Midfielder
DoB: 7 September 1987
BIRTHPLACE: Glasgow

PREMIER LEAGUE
SQUAD
19/20

11

Dead-ball specialist Snodgrass has won honours with three of the five clubs he played for before coming to West Ham. After arriving at London Stadium from Hull City in January 2017, the Scotland international was allowed to go on loan at the start of the following season to Aston Villa, where he was re-united with Steve Bruce who had signed him for Hull.

During his loan with Villa, no-one exceeded his Championship tally of 14 assists. He added seven goals of his own helping the midlands giants to the Play-Off final before coming back to West Ham and doing well enough to earn a 2019 contract extension taking up to 2021, with the possibility of an additional 12 months.

Snodgrass started his career with just over 100 games in Scotland, mostly with Livingston, but including a promotion-winning loan with Stirling Albion. He was also part of promotion-winning teams with Leeds United and Hull City, having a Premier League stint with Norwich City in between. He also won Player of the Year awards at both Elland Road and Carrow Road.

Roberto Jimenez Gago began his career in his home city of Madrid with Atletico, debuting in December 2005. Eighteen months later, he won the first of his six Under 21 caps. He was given his Hammers debut in August's Carabao Cup tie at Newport, after arriving on a free transfer from Espanyol the previous month.

After a successful loan with Gimnastic, Atletico sold Roberto to Recreativo de Huelva. Recreativo only played Roberto in the cup as they slipped to relegation and sold him back to Atletico, where he had David de Gea among others as competition for a first-team place. After three league appearances, the first at Barcelona, Roberto joined Zaragoza on loan before a summer 2010 move to Benfica. A season later he returned to Zaragoza and later played in Greece for Olympiacos where he enjoyed Champions League football. Returning to Spain, Roberto played for Espanyol and on loan to Malaga before coming to England.

ROBERTO 13

POSITION: *Goalkeeper* DoB: *10 February 1986* BIRTHPLACE: *Madrid*

Two-time Hammer of the Year, Noble was granted the Freedom of the Borough of Newham in 2016 for his services to the Borough. Other than loans to Hull City and Ipswich Town over a decade ago, Noble is a one-club man who could reach 500 games for West Ham United by the end of the 2019/20 season, which kicked-off with him 34 games short of that landmark.

Incredibly, Noble has never won a full-cap for England, probably the most astonishing omission since 'Pop' Robson, who was never capped at full level despite being the top-flight's top scorer with the Irons in 1972/73.

Noble captained England U21s in the final of the 2009 European Championships and made a total of 47 appearances for his country at every level from U16 to U21. A very composed penalty-taker, the skipper also tops 50 goals for the club he has shown such loyalty to.

Columbian international Sánchez, has played football in Uruguay, France, Spain, England (with Aston Villa) ,Italy and Spain again before joining West Ham United in 2018. He started his career in Uruguay with Danubio, becoming a professional in 2003, but had to wait until he joined River Plate of Montevideo to begin playing first-team football.

In 2007, he began a six-year spell with Valenciennes in France, at one point apparently attracting interest from the Hammers. He moved to Spanish outfit Elche in August 2013, and a year later he was transferred to Aston Villa, appearing in the FA Cup final against Arsenal at the end of his only season with them. Fiorentina in Italy was the next entry on Sánchez's CV, an initial loan being converted into a transfer prior to a subsequent loan to Espanyol.

He arrived at London Stadium after playing at the 2018 World Cup finals in Russia, having also played at the 2014 World Cup in Brazil and two Copa Americas.

Carlos SÁNCHEZ

POSITION: *Midfielder* DoB: *6 February 1986* BIRTHPLACE: *Quibdo, Colombia*

16

WEST HAM UNITED LONDON

Mark NOBLE

POSITION: *Midfielder* DoB: *8 May 1987* BIRTHPLACE: *Canning Town*

PREMIER LEAGUE
SQUAD
19/20

WEST HAM UNITED
LONDON

18

Pablo FORNALS

POSITION: Midfielder
DOB: 22 February 1996
BIRTHPLACE: Castellon de la Plana

PREMIER LEAGUE
SQUAD
19/20

A big-money signing from Villarreal in 2019 during a summer in which he won the UEFA European U21 championships with Spain, Pablo Fornals arrived at London Stadium on a five-year deal.

As a boy, Fornals had been with Villarreal and Castellon, but at the age of 16 joined Malaga who gave him his La Liga debut in what proved to be a hard-fought goalless draw at Real Madrid.

He re-joined Villarreal in 2017, for a reported fee of E12m and once again, Real Madrid figuring largely in his Spanish story. Pablo netted the only goal of the game with an audacious chip in the Yellow Submarine's first ever La Liga win away to the majestic capital club. His best goal however, came against Athletic Bilbao where he astonishingly scored with a volley from near the half-way line. His first goal for the Irons came in the 2-0 Carabao Cup victory at Newport County.

A full international, he debuted for Spain in May 2016, coming on as a late substitute in a 3-1 win over Bosnia and Herzegovina.

Jack Wilshere won his 34th cap for England in the ill-fated defeat to Iceland at Euro 2016. As of October 2019, he awaits cap number 35, although he was twice an unused sub in November 2016 while on loan from Arsenal to AFC Bournemouth, and injury forced him to withdraw from the squad in March 2018.

An academy trainee at Luton prior to joining Arsenal as a nine-year-old, he won the FA Youth Cup in 2009 after becoming the Gunners' youngest ever player when he debuted against Blackburn Rovers in September 2008, at the age of 16 years and 256 days.

He spent six months on loan to Bolton Wanderers in 2010 and eventually managed 92 Premier League starts for Arsenal, plus 33 more off the bench, before leaving the Gunners to come to West Ham United after a decade with the north London club. Like Fornals, Wilshere also scored his first Hammers goal at Newport County in the Carabao Cup in August 2019.

Jack WILSHERE 19

POSITION: **Midfielder** *DoB:* **1 January 1992** *BIRTHPLACE:* **Stevenage**

Gonçalo **CARDOSO**

POSITION: *Defender* DoB: *21 October 2000* BIRTHPLACE: *Marco de Canaveses, Portugal*

The Portugal U19 international excelled at the UEFA U19 European Championships in July as his nation reached the final. In June, he had scored with a header as Portugal eliminated England from the Toulon tournament and was subsequently brought into the West Ham fold during the summer of 2019.

A five-year contract, with an optional further year, means that Cardoso has time to develop and establish himself at West Ham, as the club's coaching staff look to hone the teenager's natural talent.

Before joining Boavista in 2017, Cardoso had been with AD Marco 09 and Penafiel. Boavista gave him a senior debut shortly before he turned 18, the tall defender making his bow against Desportivo Alves. A clean sheet in that game set the tone as shut-outs were maintained in over half of his 15 games during his first season as a senior player.

21

Angelo **OGBONNA**

POSITION: *Defender*
DoB: *23 May 1988*
BIRTHPLACE: *Cassini, Italy*

PREMIER LEAGUE SQUAD 19/20

Italy international Angelo Ogbonna was part of his nation's squad at both Euro 2012 and Euro 2016, playing against the Republic of Ireland in the latter tournament.

Having played for Nuova Cassino as a boy, he arrived at West Ham in the summer of 2015 from Juventus, having crossed the great divide from their city rivals Torino and making history in the process as the first Torino captain to move to their City rivals. While at Torino, he continued his development with a loan move to lower league Crotone.

Ogbonna made his Juve debut against Lazio in August 2013, and was quickly involved in the Champions League with his new club, soon playing in one of the competition's most iconic fixtures: Real Madrid v Juventus. Twice a Serie A winner with 'the Old Lady', Ogbonna also won the Coppa Italia in the 'double' year of 2014/15, having previously also won the Italian Super Cup.

A physically imposing and strong centre-back, Ogbonna had made 118 appearances for West Ham to the start of the 2019/20 season.

Two well-taken goals on his second appearance in claret and blue as the Hammers defeated Watford 3-1 showed what all the fuss was about after a reported club-record £45m was invested in the French U21 international.

Twenty goals in 41 appearances for Eintracht Frankfurt included an autumn purple patch that began with two goals in the 7-1 thrashing of Fortuna Dusseldorf, and continued with Haller scoring in the next six games, including a couple in the Europa League.

Although his side were well beaten, Haller marked his final game for Eintracht with a Bundesliga goal away to Bayern Munich. It was the second successive season Haller had scored at Bayern, the team he also played against as a late sub as Frankfurt won the German Cup.

Haller had arrived at Eintracht from FC Utrecht, a team he had scored for in the Play-Offs in both of his full seasons at the club. Having started with Auxerre, Haller has played for four clubs in as many countries.

Sebastien HALLER 22

POSITION: *Forward* DoB: *22 June 1994* BIRTHPLACE: *Ris-Orangis, France*

37

France U21 international Issa Diop came to London Stadium on a five-year deal from his home-town team Toulouse in 2018. He didn't get off to the best of starts, becoming the first West Ham United player to score an own-goal on his Premier League debut.

That aberration at Arsenal was not an accurate illustration of Diop's ability and he quickly addressed the balance, netting at the right end on his second appearance, an EFL Cup win over AFC Wimbledon.

Diop went on to start 33 Premier League games in his initial campaign with the Irons, establishing himself as a key member of the side in his role on the right-hand side of central-defence. A physically-imposing player, standing 6'4" tall, Issa's long-striding style enables him to cover the ground swiftly.

His footballing pedigree comes from his grandfather Lybasse Diop who played for Bordeaux in the seventies, the first Senegalese player to appear in Ligue 1.

Former England youth international and junior district sprint and triple jump champion Frederick, was snapped up on a free transfer from Fulham in the summer of 2018.

The Londoner started his career with Tottenham Hotspur, making four appearances for them, all in the Europa League. During his time with Spurs, he had loans spells with League One Brentford and both Millwall and Middlesbrough in the Championship, playing for Boro at Liverpool in an EFL cup-tie and scoring in the record-equalling penalty shoot-out, 14-13 the Merseysiders.

A move to Bristol City in 2015 proved short-lived with an almost immediate return to the capital with Fulham. He played over 100 times for the Cottagers, including the 2018 Play-Off final as his side beat Aston Villa 1-0. Fredericks was also named in the 2017/18 Championship Team of the Season.

23 Issa DIOP

POSITION: Defender DoB: 9 January 1997 BIRTHPLACE: Toulouse, France

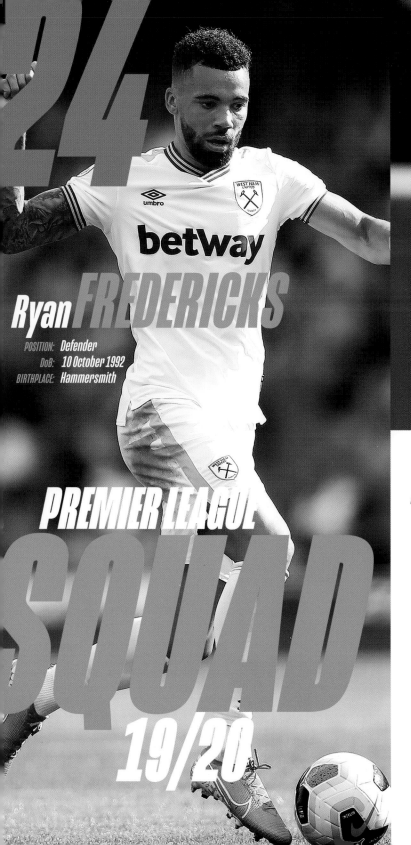

24

Ryan FREDERICKS

POSITION: *Defender*
DoB: *10 October 1992*
BIRTHPLACE: *Hammersmith*

PREMIER LEAGUE SQUAD 19/20

25

David MARTIN

POSITION: *Goalkeeper* DoB: *22 January 1986* BIRTHPLACE: *Romford*

The son of former Iron Alvin Martin, David joined from Millwall in the summer of 2019. He has plenty of big-club experience, having spent four years on Liverpool's books, albeit without getting a game for the Reds who regularly sent him out on loan.

Capped by England up to U20 level, David had been with West Ham as a youngster while also playing youth football for Tottenham and Wimbledon. It was with Wimbledon that he made his senior debut at Burnley in 2004. The Dons had moved to Milton Keynes, but not yet taken on the MK Dons name, although Martin managed games under both names for the same club.

Having moved to Liverpool, he made it as far as the bench before having loan spells to Accrington Stanley, Leicester City, Tranmere Rovers, Leeds United and Derby County. He joined MK Dons in 2010 and had seven years there, prior to two with Millwall.

Arthur MASUAKU

26

POSITION: *Defender* DoB: *7 November 1993* BIRTHPLACE: *Lille*

Masuaku is a DR Congo international, but French-born and capped by the country of his birth up to U19 level. His first goal at full international level came in June 2019 when his free-kick earned DR Congo a 1-1 draw in Kenya.

It was in August 2013 that Fuka-Arthur Masuaku Kawela made his senior debut for Valenciennes following spells during his development years with Lille and RC Lens. In 27 games, Arthur did enough to persuade Olympiacos to sign him and project him into the Champions League where the left-back made sure he got noticed by scoring against Atletico Madrid.

He continued to impress in Greece and in August 2016, following 50 league games in Greece plus 15 in European competition, West Ham brought Masuaku to London.

Albian AJETI

27

POSITION: *Forward*
DoB: *26 February 1997*
BIRTHPLACE: *Basel*

A four-year contract with an option of a further two years illustrates the club's ambition for Albian Ajeti. Signed in August 2019, the Swiss international made his debut in the Carabao Cup victory at Newport County.

The 22-year-old had already made three appearances this season before joining the Hammers, scoring against Sion in the Swiss League and PSV Eindhoven in the Champions League qualifying round.

Fifteen goals last season included one in the 6-0 Nations League destruction of Iceland on international duty. His first career goal came on his third appearance for Basel in 2014, two months after his debut which came in the Europa League. A Swiss Super League and Cup winner with Basel, who he joined as an eight-year-old, Ajeti first left his homeland to taste German football with Augsburg in 2016, before a swift return to Switzerland with St. Gallen for a season, which preceded two terms back at Basel.

The October 2019 international break saw 2016/17 Hammer of the Year winner Antonio undergo surgery following a hamstring injury sustained in the Carabao Cup win at Newport County.

Previously, a Player of the Year with Nottingham Forest, Antonio had also enjoyed promotion during his days with Sheffield Wednesday and being a Wembley winner with Southampton in the Football League Trophy.

Having started with Tooting & Mitcham United, his league debut came in 2009 at Leeds, playing for League One Cheltenham while on loan from Reading. He made his bow for the Royals the following season, soon going out on loan again, this time with Southampton. Further loans with Colchester and Sheffield Wednesday led to a transfer to the Owls, and in 2014 a move to Forest.

Called up for Sam Allardyce's only game in charge of England, Antonio was also selected by Gareth Southgate, only to have to withdraw with a troublesome hamstring injury.

Michail ANTONIO 30

POSITION: *Forward* DoB: *28 March 1990* BIRTHPLACE: *Wandsworth*

WEST HAM UNITED LONDON

4

Declan**Rice**

POSITION: *Midfielder* DoB: *14 January 1999* BIRTHPLACE: *Kingston upon Thames*

PREMIER LEAGUE
SQUAD
19/20

42

Declan Rice was voted the Hammers' Young Player of the Year for the third successive season in 2019, picking up the Players' Player of the Year award too. He also scooped the London Football Awards 2019 Young Player of the Year. Unsurprisingly, Rice is one of the hottest properties in the Premier League.

He came to West Ham as a 14-year old, having spent seven years as part of the academy at Chelsea. It was at the end of the 2016/17 campaign that he broke into the first team, being given the briefest of tastes of the Premier League football by coming on in added time in a 2–1 away win at Burnley. Since then, Rice has become one of the first names on the team sheet as well as being in demand internationally.

Having represented the Republic of Ireland (qualifying through his grandparents) three times at senior level in 2019, Rice switched his international allegiance to the country of his birth and debuted for England at Wembley against the Czech Republic.

Being the nephew of Paul Parker and cousin of Ledley King, both England internationals, Ben Johnson is a player with an impressive pedigree. His first-team debut came in February 2019 at left-back against Manchester City, the same team he had first been named on the bench against 15 months earlier.

Johnson has been with the Irons since the age of seven, and his development has seen his role change from being a flying winger to a full-back, who in the modern style understands the importance of supplementing the attack at every opportunity. He started his scholarship in the summer of 2016 and by the following February he had done well enough to step up to the PL2 side with a debut at that level against Leicester City.

Prior to his Premier League bow, Ben had gained experience in half a dozen Checkatrade Trophy fixtures and was named on the bench early in the 2019/20 season for the Carabao Cup tie at Newport County.

Ben JOHNSON 53

POSITION: *Defender* **DoB:** *24 January 2000* **BIRTHPLACE:** *London*

43

MANUEL PELLEGRINI

ISSA DIOP

2018/19 was an excellent and encouraging season for the club. Ultimately the measure of success is results, and having achieved a top-ten finish, this represented a climb of three places and an impressive ten points on the previous campaign.

Only goal difference kept the Irons from ninth position in a season when the capacity of the Hammers London Stadium was extended to 60,000. The all-round health of the club is further illustrated by the Chadwell Heath training complex redevelopment being completed and the women's team reaching their FA Cup final.

For the men's first team, there was a new and exciting start under Manuel Pellegrini. Used to high standards having been a Premier League winner and former Real Madrid boss, Pellegrini set about the task of creating a team capable of entertaining the club's 52,000 season ticket holders by playing attacking football and achieving results to go with it.

Twice the Irons transfer record was broken in order to bring in Felipe Anderson and Issa Diop while further investment in the team saw the acquisitions of Andriy Yarmolenko, Jack Wilshere, Fabián Balbuena and goalkeeper Lukasz Fabianski - who would go on to become Hammer of the Year.

As might be expected with a lot of new faces and a new approach, the team did not hit the ground running. No points were gained from the first four games.

The season started with a 4-0 loss at Liverpool against a side who would end the campaign as European champions, but it was the return to Merseyside a month later that kick-started the Londoners' season.

JACK WILSHERE

WEST HAM UNITED LONDON

FABIÁN BALBUENA

SEASON
2018/19 REVIEW

FELIPE ANDERSON

SEASON

2018/19 REVIEW

Two goals from Yarmolenko and another from Marko Arnautovic sealed a convincing 3-1 win at Everton. A solid goalless draw at home to Chelsea followed by a tremendous performance, and result, as Manchester United were beaten 3-1 in what was the game of the season.

FELIPE ANDERSON CELEBRATES
THE FIRST OF HIS BRACE V BURNLEY

MARKO ARNAUTOVIC NETS HIS SECOND AT SOUTHAMPTON

A DELIGHTED MANUEL LANZINI AT VICARAGE ROAD

That match featured the save of the season when Fabianski came over all Gordon Banks with a stunning stop to deny a towering Fellaini header.

Single goal set-backs at the hands of Brighton and Spurs slowed the revival, but five points from three games, including a four goal display against Burnley, saw the team climb to 13th position as the November international break provided an opportunity to take stock.

Despite a four-goal loss at home to eventual champions Manchester City, progression under Pellegrini was undeniable as the Irons were ignited by a four-match winning run which saw a 2-0 win at Fulham, the only game of that run where the side did not register three goals. That sequence lifted the team into the top half of the table and only two points off sixth place.

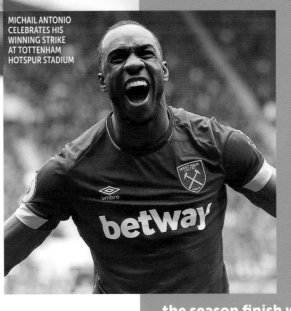

MICHAIL ANTONIO CELEBRATES HIS WINNING STRIKE AT TOTTENHAM HOTSPUR STADIUM

Defeat at home to Watford just before Christmas started a tough mid-season spell which ended with three successive defeats, meaning nine games out of 17 had been lost with just five won. Despite that run of barely a point a game in mid-season, West Ham's form since that slow start had been so solid that even after that final defeat at Manchester United, where two penalties did for the visitors, the Irons were still in eleventh place.

Ten points from the final four fixtures saw the season finish with a flourish. Only an injury-time equaliser from Leicester's Harvey Barnes prevented a second sequence of four wins in a row. Following the Foxes nicking a point, the Irons strode into Spurs' new home and emerged 1-0 victors courtesy of Michail Antonio's spectacular winner and even more spectacular celebration.

Wrapping the season up with 3-0 and 4-1 victories at home to Southampton and away to cup finalists Watford saw Marko Anautovic grab three goals in those games. This took the Austrian's tally to eleven, thereby pipping Felipe Anderson to the top scorer tag by a single strike.

MARKO ARNAUTOVIC COMPLETES THE SCORING AT GOODISON PARK

DECLAN RICE

Fabianski managed to be ever-present in the Premier League but did not appear in the cups. This enabled Diop, Antonio, Robert Snodgrass and the irrepressible Declan Rice to match the 'keeper's overall tally of 38 appearances. Topping them all was Anderson who played 40 games, 36 of them in the Premier League.

The cups brought West Ham's biggest win for 35 years, but otherwise little joy. AFC Wimbledon were met in both the Carabao and FA Cups. While there was a straightforward 3-1 win at Kingsmeadow in the Carabao Cup, there was an upset with a 4-2 defeat on the same ground later in the season, after Birmingham had been routinely overcome in the third round.

Carabao elimination came at home to Spurs, but only after six different scorers had contributed to an 8-0 victory over League Two Macclesfield at London Stadium.

As the dust settled on the season, the reality was that the team's style of play had been transformed under Pellegrini. Now, the idea was to combine a steely resolve defensively with a first thought of going forward and attacking.

To achieve this change of style while producing the results to enable a top-half finish was highly commendable in the manager's first season.

Every club expects injuries, but the Irons endured long-term absences of Manuel Lanzini, Jack Wilshere and Andriy Yarmolenko, who had made such an encouraging start, while additionally, mid-season speculation surrounding Arnautovic was another hurdle for Pellegrini to navigate. Better home form combined with a doubling of the number of away wins were important improvements.

ANGELO OGBONNA NETS NO.5

GRADY DIANGANA CELEBRATES SCORING THE EIGHTH GOAL WITH JOE POWELL

SEASON REVIEW
2018/19

ROBERT SNODGRASS

FELIPE ANDERSON

ANDRIY YARMOLENKO

WEST HAM
UNITED

LONDON

Having achieved so much in his first season, when results combined with clear signs of a successful team taking shape offered much optimism for the future, Irons fans could sense that Manuel was dreaming dreams, scheming schemes and building castles high.

49

THE LEGEND

FRANK McAVENNIE

After moving from St Mirren to West Ham United in a £340,000 deal in the summer of 1985, striker Frank McAvennie enjoyed a dream start to life in front of his new home fans. The Hammers' first home game of the season saw London rivals Queens Park Rangers provide the opposition and McAvennie turned on the style under the floodlights at the Boleyn Ground on Tuesday 20 August 1985. The new man made an instant impression on the home faithful, scoring twice in a 3-1 win as the Hammers secured their first three points of the 1985/86 campaign.

McAvennie formed an outstanding strike partnership with Tony Cottee in 1985/86 as the pair plundered a highly-impressive 46 top-flights goals. The goals of McAvennie and Cottee propelled the Hammers into a three-way race for the First Division title with Merseyside giants Liverpool and Everton. John Lyall's side ended the campaign in third place - the club's highest ever league finish. McAvennie's 26 First Division goals saw him top the Hammers' scoring charts and collect the runners-up spot in the end-of-season voting for the Hammer of the Year award.

In his second spell with the club, Frank McAvennie played his part in the Hammers' impressive run to the 1990/91 FA Cup semi-finals. With manager Billy Bonds balancing both an extended FA Cup run and a Second Division promotion push, McAvennie featured in four of the Hammers' seven FA Cup clashes. After seeing off Aldershot in the third round, they faced a trip to First Division Luton in the fourth round. The tie ended 1-1 at Kenilworth Road. McAvennie opened the scoring in the replay as he and his teammates turned on the style to win 5-0 at the Boleyn Ground. The Scot then featured in the fifth-round victory over Crewe Alexandra and the quarter-final triumph over Everton.

West Ham United won promotion back to the old First Division in 1990/91, securing the runners-up spot under the management of Billy Bonds. McAvennie hit double figures in the goalscoring charts, his ten goals helping the Hammers push eventual champions Oldham Athletic all the way. Among McAvennie's goals was a vital brace in the big London derby meeting with rivals Millwall on 24 February 1991. In front of a Boleyn Ground crowd of 20,503, McAvennie's double strike plus a Trevor Morley goal gave the Hammers a 3-1 win and ensured local bragging rights for the West Ham supporters.

Despite the team suffering relegation back to the second tier at the end of the 1991/92 campaign, McAvennie ended his second spell with the Hammers on a personal high note. His six First Division goals, ten in all competitions, could not prevent the drop and when the Hammers hosted Nottingham Forest on the final day of the season, they were already relegated. However, McAvennie still managed to sign off in style, entering the fray at the Boleyn Ground as a substitute for Mitchell Thomas, McAvennie proceeded to score a hat-trick in a 3-0 West Ham victory,

PREMIER LEAGUE 2019/20

Arsenal

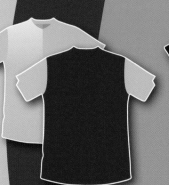

Aston Villa

Bournemouth

Brighton & Hove Albion

Burnley

Chelsea

Crystal Palace

Everton

Leicester City

Liverpool

Manchester City

Manchester United

Newcastle United

Norwich City

Sheffield United

Southampton

Tottenham Hotspur

Watford

West Ham United

Wolves

REWIND
QUIZ OF THE YEAR

20 teasers to tackle on the Hammers' 18/19 campaign...

1.
What was the score when the Hammers faced FSV Mainz 05 in the Betway Cup during the club's 2018/19 pre-season preparations?

6.

After arriving from Lazio in the summer of 2018, Felipe Anderson scored his first Premier League goal against which club?

2.
Who netted the Hammers first Premier League goal of 2018/19?

4.
Goalkeeper Lukasz Fabianski was voted Hammer of the Year in 2018/19. How many Premier League clean sheets did he keep?

7.
Who was the only Hammer to receive a red card in the league during 2018/19?

9.
Which Hammer received the most yellow cards last season?

3.
Which Hammer played in all 38 2018/19 Premier League fixtures

5.
Against which club did the Hammers record their first Premier League victory of the 2018/19 season?

8.
What was the highest London Stadium attendance of 2018/19?

10.
Who netted the final goal in West Ham's 8-0 EFL Cup demolition of Macclesfield Town?

11.
Who knocked the Hammers out of the League Cup?

13.
Which player scored the first West Ham United goal of 2019?

16.
Which player put in the most Premier League tackles for the Hammers last season?

12. - 1875

Which club did West Ham United defeat 2-0 in the FA Cup third round?

14.
How many Premier League goals did the Irons score last season?

15.
Chicharito scored seven Premier League goals last season, Felipe Anderson nine, but do you know who top-scored with ten?

17.
Who did the club sign from Benfica at the end of the 2019 January transfer window?

19.
Against which three clubs did the Hammers hit four league goals against last season?

18.
The 2018/19 season ended with a 4-1 win at which London club?

20.
Who was voted the 2018/19 Young Hammer of the Year?

ANSWERS ON PAGE 82

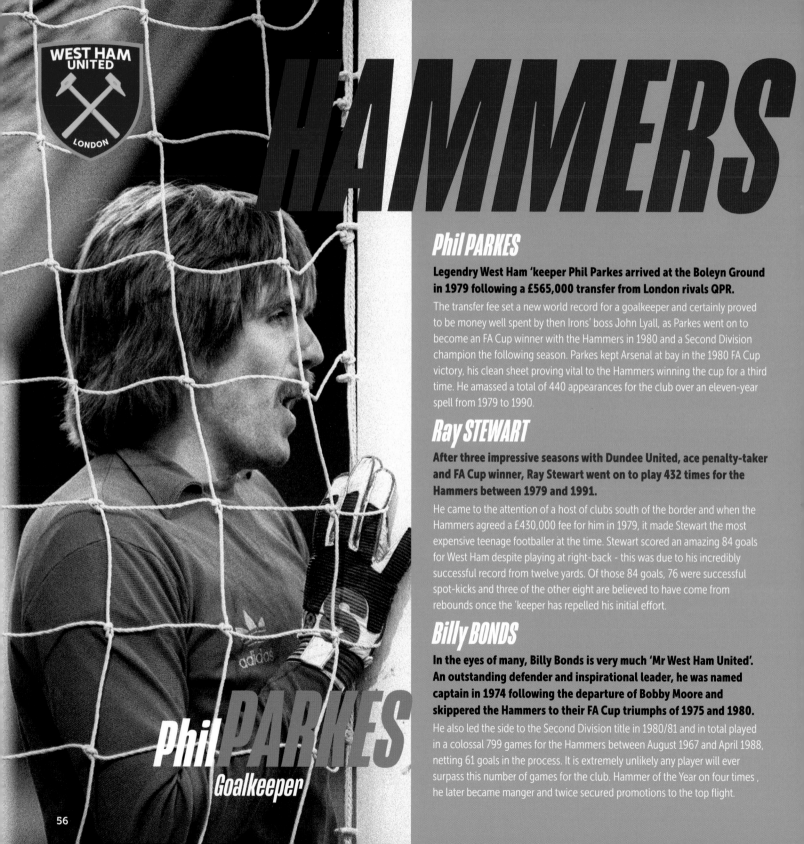

HAMMERS

Phil PARKES
Goalkeeper

Phil PARKES

Legendry West Ham 'keeper Phil Parkes arrived at the Boleyn Ground in 1979 following a £565,000 transfer from London rivals QPR.

The transfer fee set a new world record for a goalkeeper and certainly proved to be money well spent by then Irons' boss John Lyall, as Parkes went on to become an FA Cup winner with the Hammers in 1980 and a Second Division champion the following season. Parkes kept Arsenal at bay in the 1980 FA Cup victory, his clean sheet proving vital to the Hammers winning the cup for a third time. He amassed a total of 440 appearances for the club over an eleven-year spell from 1979 to 1990.

Ray STEWART

After three impressive seasons with Dundee United, ace penalty-taker and FA Cup winner, Ray Stewart went on to play 432 times for the Hammers between 1979 and 1991.

He came to the attention of a host of clubs south of the border and when the Hammers agreed a £430,000 fee for him in 1979, it made Stewart the most expensive teenage footballer at the time. Stewart scored an amazing 84 goals for West Ham despite playing at right-back - this was due to his incredibly successful record from twelve yards. Of those 84 goals, 76 were successful spot-kicks and three of the other eight are believed to have come from rebounds once the 'keeper has repelled his initial effort.

Billy BONDS

In the eyes of many, Billy Bonds is very much 'Mr West Ham United'. An outstanding defender and inspirational leader, he was named captain in 1974 following the departure of Bobby Moore and skippered the Hammers to their FA Cup triumphs of 1975 and 1980.

He also led the side to the Second Division title in 1980/81 and in total played in a colossal 799 games for the Hammers between August 1967 and April 1988, netting 61 goals in the process. It is extremely unlikely any player will ever surpass this number of games for the club. Hammer of the Year on four times , he later became manger and twice secured promotions to the top flight.

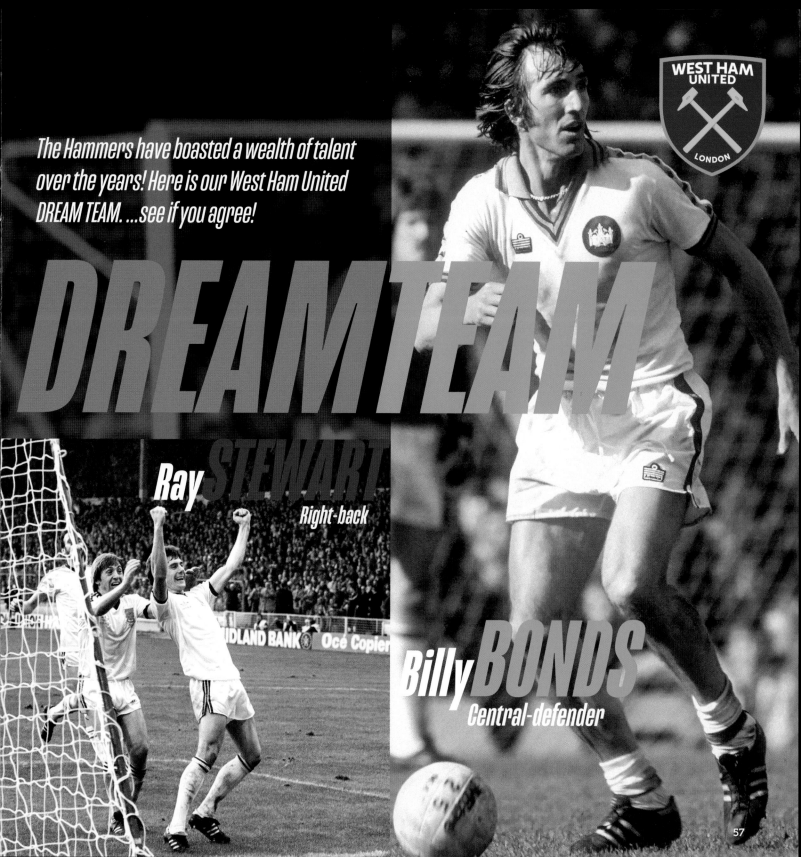

The Hammers have boasted a wealth of talent over the years! Here is our West Ham United DREAM TEAM. ...see if you agree!

DREAM TEAM

Ray STEWART
Right-back

Billy BONDS
Central-defender

HAMMERS
DREAM TEAM

Bobby **MOORE**
Central-defender

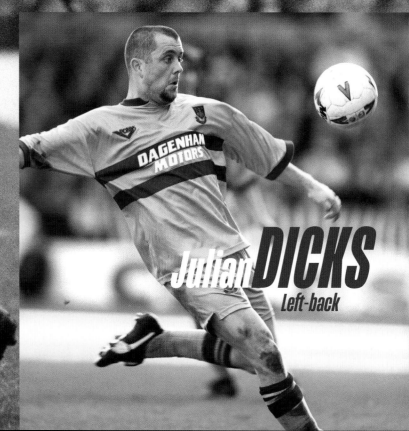

Julian **DICKS**
Left-back

Bobby MOORE

The man who finds himself named in every West Ham United dream team, Bobby Moore captained England to World Cup glory in 1966 and West Ham to FA Cup success in 1964.

A truly outstanding defender who timed his tackles to perfection, Moore appeared for the club on 647 occasions. He skippered the West Ham side to great success in the 1960s as they followed up their FA Cup win with a Charity Shield victory in 1964 and a European Cup Winners' Cup triumph in 1965. Voted Hammer of the Year on four occasions, Moore is widely recognised as the finest player ever to pull on the claret and blue shirt.

Julian DICKS

A four-time Hammer of the Year winner and West Ham cult-hero, tough-tackling left-back Julian Dicks made 365 appearances for the club between February 1988 and April 1999.

Recruited from Birmingham City in 1988 for a fee of £300,000, Dicks proceeded to make the Hammers' left-back berth his own with a series of committed performances that saw him earn the nickname of 'Terminator'. A promotion winner with West Ham in 1990/91 and again in 1992/93, Dicks then secured a high profile move to Liverpool in 1993 in a swap deal involving David Burrows and Mike Marsh. After just 13 months at Anfield he returned to West Ham in October 1994, before ending his professional playing career in 1999.

Mark WARD

Competitive and consistent, right-sided midfielder Mark Ward was a star performer for West Ham in the mid-80s. Plucked from non-league football by Oldham boss Joe Royle, Ward made his Football League debut for the Latics on the opening day of the 1983/84 season.

After two impressive seasons at Boundary Park, West Ham boss John Lyall swooped for Ward in a £250,000 deal. He enjoyed an ever-present debut season with the Hammers in 1985/86 chipping in with three First Division goals as West Ham secured a best-ever league finish of third in the top flight. A great supplier of chances to the formidable strike force of Tony Cottee and Frank McAvennie, Ward played 209 games for the Hammers before moving to Manchester City in December 1989.

Martin PETERS

England World Cup-winner and West Ham United legend Martin Peters began his trophy-laden career at the Boleyn Ground and went on to play 364 games for the club and net a century of goals in claret and blue.

Peters joined the Hammers as an apprentice in 1959, and made his senior debut in 1962. He was firmly established in the first team when West Ham won the European Cup Winners' Cup, beating TSV Munich 2-0 at Wembley in 1965. Peters won 67 full England caps, scoring in the 4-2 World Cup final victory over West Germany in 1966 in only his eighth game for his country. For both club and country he became famed for his ability to 'ghost' into goalscoring positions on the blind side of defenders.

Martin PETERS
Central-midfielder

Mark WARD
Right-Midfielder

59

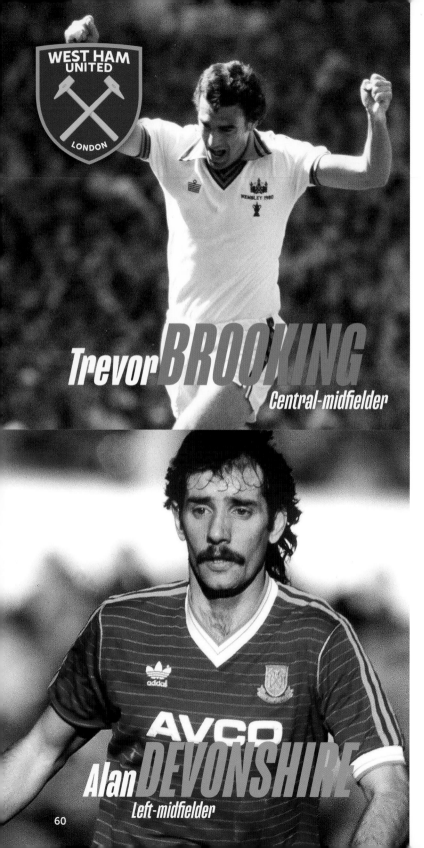

Trevor **BROOKING**

Central-midfielder

Alan **DEVONSHIRE**

Left-midfielder

Trevor BROOKING

A true West Ham icon, Trevor Brooking was born in Barking in October 1948 and the double FA Cup-winner's name is synonymous with the club, having later served as a Director and also having two brief spells as caretaker manager.

An FA Cup-winner with the Hammers in 1975, Brooking scored the only goal of the game in the Wembley final five years later, as the Hammers upset the form guide to defeat favourites Arsenal. A record five-time winner of the prestigious Hammer of the Year award, Brooking's proud Hammers playing career saw him make 643 appearances for the club and score 102 goals between 1967 and 1984.

Alan DEVONSHIRE

Alan Devonshire had a tricky route into the professional game after twice being turned away by Crystal Palace, before heading into non-league football. It was while plying his trade for Southall, he was spotted by the Hammers and signed in 1976 for a fee of £5,000, which has constantly led to him being referred to as West Ham's best-ever buy!

Devonshire's skilful wing play provided the club's fans with some iconic moments and none more so than during the successful 1979/80 FA Cup run when he was on target in the 2-1 semi-final replay victory over Everton at Elland Road. Devonshire played in a total of 448 games for the club scoring 32 goals before ending his playing days at Watford.

Geoff HURST

The hero of England's Wembley World Cup triumph in 1966 having netted a hat-trick in the 4-2 final victory over West Germany, striker Geoff Hurst scored an incredible 249 goals for West Ham United.

Born in Ashton-under-Lyne in 1941, Hurst joined West Ham as an apprentice and went on to enjoy FA Cup and European Cup Winners' Cup success at the Boleyn Ground in the mid-60s. Hurst played a vital role in the 1963/64 FA Cup triumph scoring six goals during the cup run, including the third goal in the 3-1 semi-final victory over Manchester United and the second goal in the 3-2 triumph over Preston North End at Wembley. Across 13 seasons Hurst notched 180 First Division goals and was voted Hammer of the- Year in 1965/66, 1966/67 and 1968/69.

Tony COTTEE

Born in Forest Gate in July 1965, popular striker Tony Cottee began his career with West Ham and proved to be a consistent goalscorer at both youth and reserve team level.

It was of little surprise that he was handed his first-team debut at the age of just 17 and unsurprisingly, he marked the occasion with a goal as the Hammers registered a 3-0 New Year's Day victory over Spurs at the Boleyn Ground in 1983. Cottee formed an excellent striking partnership with Frank McAvennie and in 1985/86 the double act went on to yield an incredible 46 league goals as the Hammers stood toe-to-toe with Merseyside giants Liverpool and Everton in a three-way race for the title. Across two spells with the club, Cottee made a total of 336 appearances, netting 146 goals.

HAMMERS DREAM TEAM

WEST HAM UNITED
LONDON

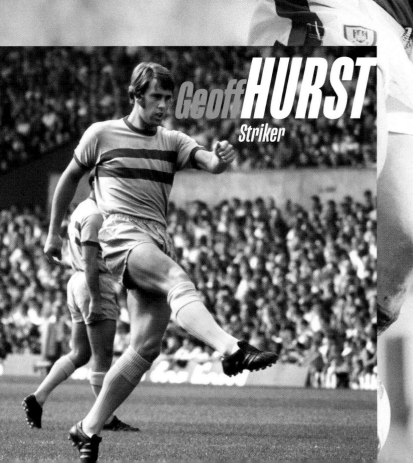

Geoff HURST
Striker

Tony COTTEE
Striker

CARLOS *TEVEZ*

West Ham fans really got to see the best of Argentinean genius Carlos Tevez once Alan Curbishley had been appointed boss at the Boleyn Ground. With the Hammers fighting for Premier League survival in 2006/07, Tevez really turned on the style in a thrilling London derby match at home to Tottenham Hotspur on 4 March 2007. Tevez created the opening goal for Mark Noble then scored his first goal for the club to put the Hammers 2-0 up at the break. Despite setting up Bobby Zamora for the Hammers' third goal, his man of the match display could not prevent a heartbreaking 4-3 defeat.

Boosted by the spirited showing against Spurs, and in particular the quality of Tevez's performance, West Ham ended a five-match Premier League losing streak, pulling off a vital 2-1 win away to Blackburn Rovers on 17 March 2007. Trailing 1-0 to a Christopher Samba goal early in the second half, the Hammers were handed a route back into the game when they were awarded a penalty 19 minutes from time. Tevez took the responsibility of calmly converting the spot-kick and West Ham snatched victory from the jaws of defeat when Bobby Zamora sealed a 2-1 win.

With Tevez really pulling the strings, West Ham's 'Great Escape' was well and truly underway with the team having won five of their previous seven Premier League games, they faced another crucial fixture when Bolton Wanderers provided the opposition in the final home game of the 2006/07 campaign. In a highly charged atmosphere, the Hammers, and Tevez in particular, were quick out of the blocks in this must-win game. The Argentinean fired West Ham in front after just ten minutes and when he made it 2-0 eleven minutes later, the celebrations almost rocked the foundations of the Boleyn Ground. Curbishley's Tevez-inspired side won the game 3-1 and went into the final game of the season knowing a point would guarantee survival.

Having been the two-goal hero against Bolton the previous weekend, Tevez took his place in the West Ham line-up for the final game of the 2006/07 season away to Premier League champions Manchester United. The situation was simple for the Hammers, they knew a point would ensure Premier League status for 2007/08. Attempting to thwart the champions at Old Trafford was a massive challenge, but one that West Ham certainly rose to. Not only did they secure the point they craved, they went one better by winning that match 1-0. The only goal of the game came from the Hammers' talisman Tevez on the stroke of half-time.

Having made such an influential contribution to West Ham's incredible escape from the drop, the fans voted Carlos Tevez their Hammer of the Year for 2006/07. Tevez was certainly the driving force and the touch of class that the Hammers needed as they demonstrated phenomenal end-of-season form by winning seven of their final nine Premier League fixtures. Tevez only played for West Ham United for one season, but there can be few players in the club's history that have had such an impact in such a short space of time.

THE LEGEND

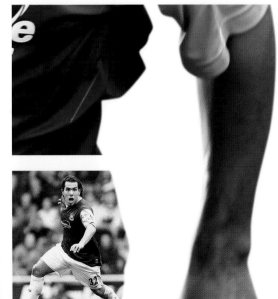

PREMIER LEAGUE 2

SEAN ADARKWA

POSITION: Forward   **DOB:** 11/10/00

With the Irons since the age of eleven, Adarkwa has been mentored by Carlton Cole, having been spotted playing for the Dagenham and Redbridge District side. He signed his first professional contract in May 2019.

OLADAPO AFOLAYAN

POSITION: Forward   **DOB:** 12/02/98

Afolayan started at Chelsea and continued with Toronto, after emigrating to Canada, before coming to West Ham via Solihull Moors, who he played for while studying for a civil engineering degree. Made his league debut on loan to Oldham last season.

OLATUNJI *AKINOLA*

POSITION: Defender   **DOB:** 21/11/98

The highly-rated centre-back has been progressing through the 'Academy of Football' since he was eight. Akinola was only 15 when he made his U18 debut in 2014 before making his Development team bow as a 16-year-old the following year.

CONOR *COVENTRY*

POSITION: Midfielder   **DOB:** 25/03/00

The winner of the Dylan Tombides award in 2017/18, Conor is a Republic of Ireland international who plays as a holding midfielder. He made his first-team debut in the stunning 8-0 EFL Cup win over Macclesfield in 2018.

JOSEPH *ANANG*

POSITION: Goalkeeper   **DOB:** 08/06/00

Anang came to West Ham as a scholar in July 2017. He has been called up by England at U19 level, travelled to first-team games as part of the Hammers' squad and played for the club in the Checkatrade Trophy.

MESAQUE *DJU*

POSITION: Forward   **DOB:** 18/03/99

Dju has been with the Hammers since January 2019, having had eight years with Benfica after starting out at Amadora CF. A Portugal U20 international, he was named in the European U19 Championships Team of the Tournament in 2017.

ANOUAR EL MHASSANI

POSITION: Midfielder   **DOB:** 18/04/01

El Mhassani joined West Ham from Ajax on a three-year deal in 2017. A left-footed attack-minded creator, he had been with the Amsterdam giants for eight years after beginning his career with Zeebrugge.

NATHAN HOLLAND

POSITION: Midfielder   **DOB:** 19/06/98

The winger made his first-team debut in an EFL cup-tie with Bolton in September 2017. Holland, who has been capped by England up to U19 level, joined West Ham United from Everton nine months before his debut.

REECE HANNAM

POSITION: Defender   **DOB:** 11/09/00

Hannam already had 22 U18 appearances under his belt before he had left school and became a scholar with the Irons in 2017. The left-back, who loves to get forward and provide assists, made his PL2 debut as a 16-year old.

DAN KEMP

POSITION: Midfielder   **DOB:** 11/01/99

Kemp, a forward-thinking player who can operate in a wide or central position, was with Chelsea from the age of six to 16. Now an England U20 international, he helped his country win the Toulon Trophy in 2017.

ALFIE LEWIS

POSITION: Midfielder   DOB: 28/09/99

Lewis is a highly-regarded schemer who has been with the Hammers since he was nine-years-old, and first appeared in PL2 when he was only 16. He has also been a regular in EFL Trophy matches.

EMMANUEL LONGELO

POSITION: Forward   DOB: 27/12/00

Longelo has been with West Ham since he was ten, and for his first seven seasons, had his older brother Rosaire alongside him, before big brother left for Newcastle. A winger, Emmanuel has played for the Irons in the Checkatrade Trophy.

PREMIER 2 LEAGUE

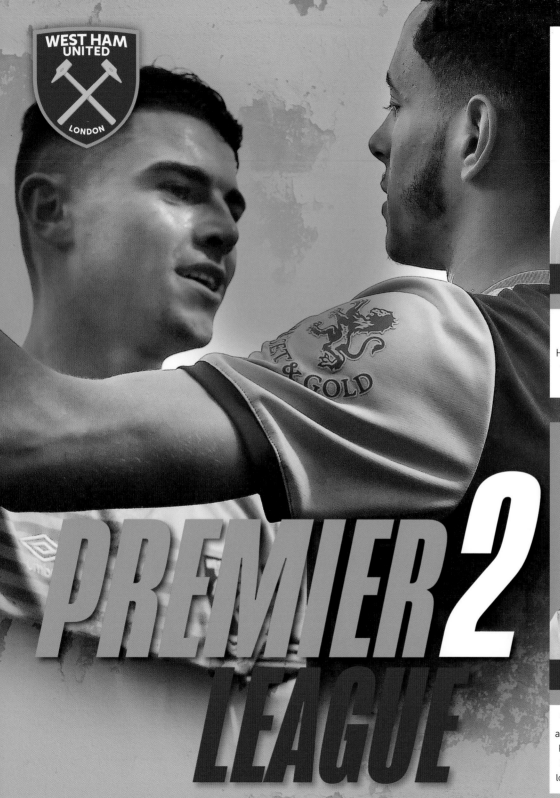

PREMIER 2 LEAGUE

JEREMY NGAKIA

POSITION: Midfielder   DOB: 07/09/00

Ngakia is a pacey right-sided midfielder who can play attacking and defensive flank roles. He began his scholarship in 2017 after regularly featuring at U18 level while still at school and debuted at U23 level against Spurs in 2018.

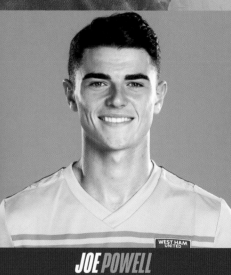

JOE POWELL

POSITION: Midfielder   DOB: 30/10/98

The versatile academy product, who can operate across the midfield, is also comfortable at left-back. Powell claimed two assists on his first-team debut in the 8-0 win over Macclesfield, before going on loan to Northampton for the remainder of 2018/19.

BERNARDO ROSA

POSITION: Midfielder   **DOB:** 20/09/00

Right-winger Rosa made his U18 and U23 debuts within a few weeks of each other late in 2016 against Tottenham Hotspur and Blackburn Rovers respectively. He also scored a hat-trick against Norwich at U18 level in 2018.

XANDE SILVA

POSITION: Forward   **DOB:** 16/03/97

Silva joined West Ham in 2018 after four years in Portugal with Vitoria Guimaraes. Quickly made an impact with a four-minute hat-trick against Spurs in the opening PL2 fixture of 2018/19. He made his first-team debut at Burnley in December 2018.

ANTHONY SCULLY

POSITION: Midfielder   **DOB:** 03/12/99

The son of former Queens Park Rangers and Notts County winger Tony, Anthony has been with the Irons since 2011 and has been capped by the Republic of Ireland at every level up to U19.

LOUIE WATSON

POSITION: Midfielder   **DOB:** 06/07/01

The Republic of Ireland U18 international schemer first played for the Irons U18s when he was only 15, and signed his first professional contract in May 2019. His father Steve captained Farnborough Town against Arsenal in the FA Cup in 2003.

FAN'TASTIC

There are five Great Sporting Brits hiding in the crowd... Can you find them?

ANSWERS ON PAGE 82

WEST HAM UNITED LONDON

THE HAMMERS ACADEMY

IYIOLA ADEBAYO
POSITION: Midfielder **DOB:** 07/09/02

Adebayo is an intelligent midfielder with an eye for a clever pass. He agreed a two-year scholarship with West Ham United in April 2019, three months after making his U18 debut as a substitute in a 2-0 win against Swansea City.

MICHAEL ADU
POSITION: Midfielder **DOB:** 13/10/02

Midfielder Adu began his West Ham United scholarship in the summer of 2019, but had been on the Hammers' radar since the summer of 2015 when he was part of an Irons U14 team that topped its group in a tournament in Paris.

KEENAN APPIAH-FORSON
POSITION: Midfielder **DOB:** 16/10/01

Having begun his scholarship in the summer of 2018, Appiah-Forson quickly found his way into the U23 side, debuting against Everton a fortnight before his 17th birthday - the first of 15 games at U23 level in his first season.

HARRISON ASHBY
POSITION: Defender **DOB:** 14/11/01

Ashby made his Scotland U19 debut, as a second-half substitute against Japan, in September. He then made his first start in the repeat fixture a few days later, and rounded off a great week with his West Ham U23 debut against Valencia 'B', a day after returning from International Duty.

SAM CAIGER

POSITION: Defender **DOB:** 30/04/02

Along with five other members of the current U18 squad, Caiger was part of the Hammers U14 group who impressed in Paris in 2015, before losing to Braga in the knock-out stage of a tournament in which they had been group winners.

KAI CORBETT

POSITION: Midfielder **DOB:** 08/10/02

England U15 international Corbett grabbed the headlines during the Generation Adidas Cup in Texas in 2019, with four goals in as many games, including the opening goal in the thrilling extra-time victory over LA Galaxy.

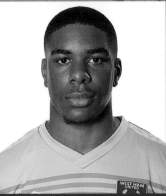

JAYDEN FEVRIER

POSITION: Defender **DOB:** 14/04/03

The versatile England U16 international debuted at U18 level in November 2017 when he was only 15. He stepped up to U23 level eleven months later as a substitute in the 3-0 Premier League 2 fixture at Leicester City on 26 October 2018.

WILL GREENIDGE

POSITION: Defender **DOB:** 15/05/02

Full-back Greenidge caught the eye as a 15-year-old playing in the Premier League International Cup against Benfica in 2017. He made seven U18 appearances while still at school, before starting his West Ham United scholarship in 2018.

DANIEL CHESTERS

POSITION: Midfielder **DOB:** 04/04/02

The midfield schemer debuted at U23 level against Liverpool in February 2018, before beginning his two-year scholarship in the summer. His career took another upward step with a Checkatrade Trophy appearance at Yeovil in November 2018.

AMADOU DIALLO

POSITION: Forward **DOB:** 15/02/03

Highly-rated England U16 international Diallo is used to playing above his age level. He was only 14 years of age when he made his U18 debut in 2017 against Arsenal, and in 2018, he scored against Manchester City at U18 level.

JAKE GIDDINGS

POSITION: Midfielder **DOB:** 07/11/01

Defensive-midfielder Giddings started learning his trade from Mark Noble as a 13-year-old, when the Hammers skipper, who also has a history of coming through the West Ham ranks, led sessions for the club's Academy players.

BENJAMIN HEAL

POSITION: Midfielder **DOB:** 09/10/02

A talented midfielder with great potential, Heal joined West Ham United's Academy on a two-year deal from non league Cambridge City as a 16-year old, after coming to prominence under City coach Mark Pleasants from U14 level upwards.

THE HAMMERS ACADEMY

GAEL KILEBA

POSITION: Midfielder **DOB:** 11/11/02

Attack-minded Kileba was first named on the bench in January 2018 for a fixture with Fulham, shortly after his 15th birthday. His performances in the 2019 Generation Adidas Cup, where the Hammers progressed to the semi-final, really caught the eye.

SAM NSUMBU

POSITION: Defender **DOB:** 30/04/02

Able to play at full-back or centre-back, Nsumbu was first spotted playing schools football for Barking & Dagenham. He signed a scholarship with the Hammers in the summer of 2018, and made his U18 debut against Spurs in September 2018.

KRISZTIAN HEGYI

POSITION: Goalkeeper **DOB:** 24/09/02

Widely regarded as one of the brightest prospects in Europe, Hungary U17 international goalkeeper Hegyi joined the Academy of Football from Haladas, and made his U18s debut against Brighton & Hove Albion in April.

DANIEL JINADU

POSITION: Goalkeeper **DOB:** 21/06/02

England U16 international Jinadu, spent time with Chelsea before joining West Ham United in December 2017 and taking up a two-year scholarship in the summer of 2018. He made his U18 Premier League Hammers debut against Arsenal in January 2018.

SEBASTIAN NEBYLA

POSITION: Midfielder **DOB:** 25/02/01

After beginning his career with Startaka Trnava, tall attacking midfielder Nebyla came to London in the summer of 2018. The U17 Slovakia international quickly stepped up to Premier League 2 and has also gained experience in the Checkatrade Trophy.

JOSH OKOTCHA

POSITION: Defender **DOB:** 19/12/01

Centre-back Okotcha began his scholarship with West Ham in the summer of 2018. He made ten U18 starts while still a schoolboy, and his ability was rewarded with a PL2 debut at home to Sunderland on 5 February 2018, just two months after his 16th birthday.

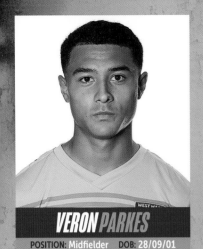

VERON PARKES

POSITION: Midfielder **DOB:** 28/09/01

Parkes arrived at the club from Crystal Palace in December 2017, and debuted for the Irons at U18 level the following month. He began the 2018/19 campaign in blistering form for the U18s, and then netted in his first two games for the U23s.

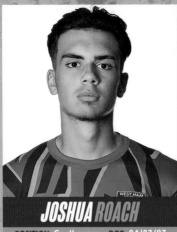

JOSHUA ROACH

POSITION: Goalkeeper **DOB:** 04/03/03

Called up to an England U15 training camp in 2015, Roach agreed a two-year scholarship with the Irons in April 2019. He won the County Cup with his school Aldenham, before going on to be selected for Herts and Essex U13s.

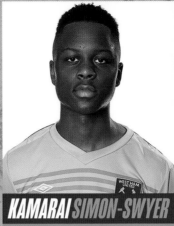

KAMARAI SIMON-SWYER

POSITION: Midfielder **DOB:** 04/12/02

After heading the winner in the 2019 Generation Adidas Cup quarter-final 2-1 triumph over LA Galaxy in Texas, Simon-Swyer made his first U18 appearance of the 2019/20 campaign in an early season 2-1 victory over Swansea City.

BRANDON THOMAS

POSITION: Defender **DOB:** 01/11/02

Right-back Thomas was still in the U15s when he first came onto the U18 scene against Chelsea in November 2017. Not to be confused with near namesake Thomas Brandon who played in the same position for the Irons before the First World War.

LENNON PEAKE

POSITION: Midfielder **DOB:** 22/07/02

Winger Peake first came to prominence in the 2015 U14 CSAKBFoot tournament in Paris. He signed his two-year scholarship in the summer of 2018, and made his U18 Premier League debut as a substitute in the 4-1 win at Fulham on 1 September 2018.

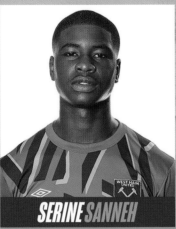

SERINE SANNEH

POSITION: Goalkeeper **DOB:** 20/11/02

Selected by England at U16 and U17 level before leaving school, Sanneh was just 15 years and four months when he made his West Ham U18 debut in a 2-1 win over Leicester City on 10 February 2018. Amazingly, he had been on the U18 bench when still an U13.

PETER STROUD

POSITION: Midfielder **DOB:** 23/04/02

USA U17 international Stroud, arrived from New York Red Bulls in summer 2018 and debuted in a 1-0 U18 Premier League victory at Swansea City in August 2018, before making his U23 bow as a substitute against the same club in Premier League 2 two months later.

CHRISTIAN VELIKY

POSITION: Midfielder **DOB:** 14/01/03

Talented right-footed attacking midfielder Veliky joined West Ham United from Czech Republic outfit Slavia Prague during the summer of 2019 after a successful trial with the Hammers late the previous season.

FAST FORWARD

One thing's for certain, 2019/20 is going to be a great season, but where are the trophies heading?

See if you agree with our predictions.

PREMIER LEAGUE WINNERS
Liverpool

PREMIER LEAGUE TOP SCORER
Mo Salah

PREMIER LEAGUE RUNNERS-UP
Manchester City

RELEGATED TO THE CHAMPIONSHIP: 18TH
Wolves

RELEGATED TO THE CHAMPIONSHIP: 19TH
Aston Villa

BOTTOM OF THE PREMIER LEAGUE
Newcastle United

FA CUP WINNERS
West Ham United

FA CUP RUNNERS-UP
Tottenham Hotspur

LEAGUE CUP WINNERS
Leicester City

LEAGUE CUP RUNNERS-UP
Liverpool

CHAMPIONSHIP WINNERS

Leeds United

CHAMPIONSHIP RUNNERS-UP

Middlesbrough

CHAMPIONSHIP PLAY-OFF WINNERS

Cardiff City

CHAMPIONSHIP TOP SCORER

Patrick Bamford

LEEDS UNITED

HAMMERS' TOP SCORER

Felipe Anderson

HAMMER OF THE YEAR

Declan Rice

CHAMPIONS LEAGUE WINNERS

Manchester City

CHAMPIONS LEAGUE RUNNERS-UP

Barcelona

EUROPA LEAGUE WINNERS

Arsenal

EUROPA LEAGUE RUNNERS-UP

Sevilla

WEST HAM UNITED

WEST HAM UNITED WOMEN

KATHARINA BAUNACH

POSITION: Defender   DOB: 18/01/89

German international Baunach played almost 300 games for Bayern Munich, winning the Bundesliga in 2015 and domestic cups in 2011 and 2012. Even more success came with Wolfsburg where she did the double in both 2018 and 2019.

JACYNTA GALABADAARACHCHI

POSITION: Forward   DOB: 06/07/91

Following a brief spell with Melbourne, where she became a W-League champion, Galabadaarachchi moved to Perth Glory in 2018, and reached the W-League Grand final. The Australia U17 international joined West Ham United in July 2019.

COURTNEY BROSNAN

POSITION: Goalkeeper   DOB: 10/11/95

Signed from Le Havre in August 2019, Brosnan had spent two years in France, starting with Ambilly Feminin. Called up by the USA at U23 level, she also qualifies for Ireland and has represented the Republic up to U19 level.

BROOKE HENDRIX

POSITION: Defender   DOB: 06/05/93

After starting her career in the USA, tall central defender Hendrix also played football in Holland, Scotland (with Rangers), Switzerland, Iceland and Italy before arriving at West Ham, adding an FA Cup final appearance to one for Brescia in the final of the Coppa Italia.

KENZA DALI

POSITION: Midfielder   DOB: 31/07/91

A France international who reached the World Cup quarter-final in 2015, Dali joined West Ham United in July 2019, from Dijon. She started her career with Olympique Lyon and Rodez, before five seasons with PSG prior to a second spell with Lyon.

LEANNE KIERNAN

POSITION: Forward   DOB: 27/04/99

While Kiernan's cup final hat-trick, helped Shelbourne win the Irish double in 2016, another cup hat-trick came the Republic of Ireland international's way in West Ham colours last season against Huddersfield Town en-route to the FA Cup final.

ESMEE DE GRAAF

POSITION: Forward   DOB: 02/08/97

After three seasons with PEC Zwolle, Dutch international striker De Graaf netted three times in 13 games during her first season with the Irons, before an ACL injury sustained in December ruled her out for the remainder of the campaign.

CECILIE KVAMME

POSITION: Defender   DOB: 11/09/95

In the summer of 2019, after six seasons with Arna-Bjornar and half a campaign with Sandviken, Norway international Kvamme swapped football in her native country for the opportunity to test herself in the Women's Super League with the Hammers.

GILL FLAHERTY

POSITION: Defender   DOB: 24/08/91

England international Flaherty arrived at West Ham with a wealth of experience and silverware gained at Arsenal and Chelsea. She scored her first Hammers goal in a draw against former side Chelsea, and led the Irons out at Wembley in the 2019 FA Cup final.

ALISHA LEHMAN

POSITION: Forward   DOB: 21/01/99

Lehman debuted for Young Boys in 2016 and joined West Ham United two years later. Ever-present in her first season with the Irons, the Swiss star's nine goals earned Lehman a nomination for the PFA Women's Young Player of the Year award.

ADRIANA LEON

POSITION: Forward   **DOB:** 02/10/92

After gaining extensive experience in Switzerland as well as her own country, Canada international Leon moved to West Ham in January 2019. Making ten appearances and scoring three goals, she also started the 2019 FA Cup final against Manchester City.

JULIA SIMIC

POSITION: Midfielder   **DOB:** 14/05/89

During her first season in England, Simic chipped in with three goals and four assists from her 15 appearances, before a knee injury curtailed her campaign. A German international, Simic was a two-time German cup winner with Bayern Munich and Wolfsburg.

KATE LONGHURST

POSITION: Midfielder   **DOB:** 02/05/89

Having started with Colchester and subsequently played for Watford and Chelsea and Liverpool, Longhurst joined West Ham United in 2018. Twice a WSL winner with the Reds, she also scored in the 2012 FA Cup final for Chelsea.

ERIN SIMON

POSITION: Defender   **DOB:** 19/08/94

A versatile defender, Erin played college football for Syracuse Orange in New York before joining West Ham from Sky Blue FC during the summer of 2018. An encouraging first season with the Hammers brought 22 appearances, including every FA Cup game.

TESSEL MIDDAG

POSITION: Midfielder   **DOB:** 23/12/92

Former Manchester City player Middag, who began her career with AVV Swift, later won both league and cup in the Netherlands with ADO Den Haag, and the cup again with Ajax. The Dutch international unfortunately missed all of last season due to an ACL injury.

CHO SO-HYUN

POSITION: Midfielder   **DOB:** 24/06/88

A four-time title winner in her own country, So-Hyun is the record appearance maker for her nation, capped 115 times. After joining West Ham in January 2019, she scored the all-important penalty in the shoot-out win over Reading to send the Irons to the FA Cup final.

ANNA MOORHOUSE

POSITION: Goalkeeper   **DOB:** 30/03/95

Having previously played for Everton, Durham and Doncaster Belles as a youngster, 'keeper Moorhouse swapped Arsenal for West Ham United in the summer of 2018, and made 16 appearances in her first season with the Hammers.

MARTHA THOMAS

POSITION: Forward   **DOB:** 31/05/96

American forward Thomas made the move to West Ham United in July 2019 from French side Le Havre AC. Born in England, she moved to Florida at the age of six, where her excellent form for college side Charlotte 49ers led to her return to Europe.

VYAN SAMPSON

POSITION: Defender   **DOB:** 02/07/96

Sampson debuted for Arsenal as a teenager and enjoyed seven years with the north London club prior to arriving at West Ham in 2018. A former England U19 international, Sampson made 19 appearances in her first season with the Irons.

LAURA VETTERLEIN

POSITION: Defender   **DOB:** 07/04/92

The two times Champions League and Bundesliga winner made the move to the Irons from SC Sand in July 2019. Left-footed centre-half Vetterlein has represented Germany up to U20 level and won the European U17 Championship with her nation in 2009.

ALAN TAYLOR

Striker Alan Taylor enjoyed the perfect West Ham United debut after joining the Hammers from Fourth Division Rochdale in December 1974. The step up from the Fourth Division to the First Division may have been daunting, but Taylor enjoyed the ideal start to life with the Hammers, appearing as a substitute in a 2-1 victory over Division One champions Leeds United at the Boleyn Ground on 7 December 1974. Stepping out in front of a crowd of 39,562 was certainly a memorable moment for Taylor and a far cry from the sparsely populated terraces of Spotland.

In only his fifth appearance and second start in a West Ham shirt following his £40,000 switch from Rochdale, Taylor swiftly won the hearts of the West Ham fans as he scored both goals the Hammers' epic FA Cup quarter-final victory over Arsenal at Highbury. In front of a crowd 56,742 on 8 March 1975, Taylor's brace provided the Hammers with sweet revenge having suffered a 3-0 First Division defeat at the same venue some five months earlier. Taylor's double-strike booked the Hammers a semi-final date with Ipswich Town and saw the striker's name etched into West Ham FA Cup folklore.

Alan Taylor was once again the cup hero as the Hammers booked their place in the 1975 FA Cup final. After their initial semi-final against Ipswich Town at Villa Park had ended goalless, Taylor netted twice in the Stamford Bridge replay to seal a 2-1 win and book a Wembley date with Fulham. Taylor's two goals made him the toast of East London and also made him extremely popular with teammate Billy Jennings who must have feared the worst after his own goal had given the Suffolk side a route back into the replay. However, Taylor's second goal of the night saved Jennings' blushes and took the Hammers to Wembley.

After two goals in the quarter-final and a second brace in the semi-final success at Stamford Bridge, Taylor's magic touch in the cup continued as he proceeded to score twice in the final. Alan Taylor had gained the reputation as the man whose goals had taken the Hammers to Wembley, so it was somewhat fitting that he was again on target in the final too. The 1975 FA Cup final is now the match which Taylor is always so fondly remembered for, his second-half strikes after 60 and 64 minutes securing a 2-0 triumph over Fulham and bringing the famous old trophy back to the Boleyn for the second time in the club's history.

After his FA Cup goalscoring heroics in 1974/75, Taylor continued his fine form in front of goal for the Hammers when he was the club's leading scorer in 1975/76. Taylor ended the campaign with 17 goals and was on target in the memorable European Cup Winners' Cup campaign. He netted against Ararat Erevan in the second round and Den Haag in round three, before appearing in the final as a substitute, replacing Frank Lampard (Snr). In total, Alan Taylor scored 36 goals for West Ham United in 124 games for the club between December 1974 and May 1979.

ANSWERS

PAGE 54: REWIND QUIZ OF THE YEAR

1. 1-1. West Ham won 7-6 on penalties.
2. Marko Arnautovic.
3. Lukasz Fabianski.
4. 7.
5. Everton away, 3-1.
6. Manchester United.
7. Mark Noble.
8. 59,988 v Everton.
9. Robert Snodgrass, 10.
10. Grady Diangana.
11. Tottenham Hotspur.
12. Birmingham City.
13. Marko Arnautovic.
14. 52.
15. Marko Arnautovic.
16. Declan Rice, 98.
17. Mesaque Dju.
18. Watford.
19. Burnley, Huddersfield Town and Watford.
20. Declan Rice.

PAGE 70: FAN'TASTIC

Owen Farrell, Lewis Hamilton Johanna Konta, Anthony Joshua and Ben Stokes.